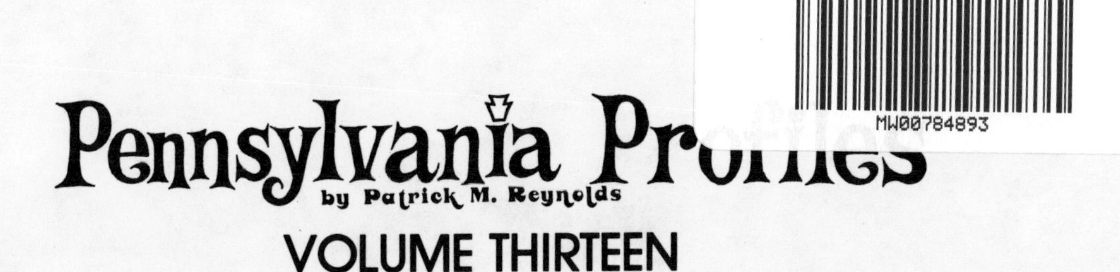
MW00784893

Pennsylvania Profiles

by Patrick M. Reynolds

VOLUME THIRTEEN

The Johnstown Flood

and Other Stories by Patrick M. Reynolds

Published by

The Red Rose Studio
Willow Street, PA 17584

ISBN O-932514-20-0

The Red Rose Studio publishes many other books by Patrick M. Reynolds including the Texas Lore collection and Big Apple Almanac. For a catalog, send $1.00 to The Red Rose Studio, The Town of Willow Street. PA 17584.

Printed in the U.S.A.

Dedicated to
Paul Almer

Corporal, Pennsylvania State Police
Major, Pennsylvania Army National Guard
A fellow Vietnam War veteran and my friend.

PENNSYLVANIA
STATE
POLICE

I took this photo of Paul and my children a few months before he was killed in the line of duty with the State Police in April, 1989.

Introduction

Pennsylvania Profiles is a syndicated cartoon and each page of this book first appeared in the following publications across the Commonwealth between March, 1988 and July, 1989:

Beaver County Times
Brookville American
Centennial Reports
Columbia News
Dubois Courier-Express
Erie Sunday Times-News
Greensburg Sunday Tribune-Review
Harrisburg Sunday Patriot-News
Huntingdon Daily News
Johnstown Tribune-Democrat
Lebanon Daily News
Mount Joy Merchandiser
Pennsylvania Magazine
Pottsville Republican
Quarryville Sun-Ledger
Reading Sunday Eagle
The (Scranton) Scrantonian
Sunbury Daily Item
Warren Times-Observer
York Dispatch

About the page numbering . . .

This book is part of the **Pennsylvania Profiles** series and the page numbers pick up where **Volume 12** ended. To obtain a catalog of the other **Pennsylvania Profiles** books, and Mr. Reynolds' series on Texas and New York City, send $1.00 to The Red Rose Studio, 358 Flintlock Drive, Willow Street, PA 17584.

The South Fork Dam,

14 MILES UPSTREAM FROM JOHNSTOWN, WAS BUILT TO SUPPLY WATER TO THE PENNSYLVANIA CANAL SYSTEM DURING DRY SPELLS. BEFORE IT WAS COMPLETED,

THE RAILROAD MADE THE CANAL OBSOLETE. IN 1852 THE PENNSYLVANIA RAILROAD PURCHASED THE CANAL PROPERTIES FROM THE STATE FOR $7½ MILLION. THE SOUTH FORK DAM WAS PART OF THE PACKAGE.

THE SOUTH FORK FISHING AND HUNTING CLUB WAS FORMED IN 1879. ITS MEMBERS WERE SUPER-RICH BUSINESSMEN FROM PITTSBURGH, INCLUDING...

Andrew Mellon
Robert Pitcairn
Henry Clay Frick
Andrew Carnegie
Philander C. Knox

THE CLUB BOUGHT THE SOUTH FORK DAM AND CONVERTED LAKE CONEMAUGH BEHIND IT INTO A FANCY SUMMER RESORT WITH 20 PRIVATE VICTORIAN COTTAGES AND A HUGE CLUBHOUSE.

BUT THE MILLIONAIRES SKIMPED ON REPAIRS AND RENOVATIONS ON THE 75 FT.-HIGH DAM. THE WORK WAS SLIPSHOD AND THE WALL SAGGED IN THE MIDDLE WHERE IT SHOULD HAVE BEEN HIGHER. IT WAS A DISASTER WAITING TO HAPPEN.

ON MAY 31, 1889, IT HAD BEEN RAINING HEAVILY FOR HOURS. THE WATER IN LAKE CONEMAUGH WAS RISING AN INCH EVERY 10 MINUTES. THE SOUTH FORK DAM WAS ABOUT TO CAUSE **THE JOHNSTOWN FLOOD.**

Cambria County
WAS GROWING RAPIDLY IN THE MID 1800'S. LUMBER WAS NEEDED TO BUILD HOUSES, SO DEVELOPERS STRIPPED THE TIMBER OFF ITS MOUNTAINS AND HILLS.

WITH NO ROOT SYSTEM TO ABSORB IT, RAIN WATER RACED DOWN THE MOUNTAINS, TEARING AWAY MOST OF THE GROUND COVER.

RIVER CHANNELS IN THE CONEMAUGH VALLEY WERE NARROWED TO MAKE ROOM FOR MORE BUILDINGS.

CONSEQUENTLY, THE CITY OF **JOHNSTOWN** HAD RARELY GONE THROUGH A YEAR WITHOUT WATER IN ITS STREETS.

THERE HAD BEEN BAD FLOODS IN 1885, '87 AND '88.

MAY 30, 1889: A HEAVY STORM HITS WESTERN AND CENTRAL PENNSYLVANIA, DUMPING 8 INCHES OF RAIN IN 24 HOURS.

BY EARLY MORNING, **MAY 31, 1889,** THE LOWER SECTION OF JOHNSTOWN IS UNDER WATER. AT 11 A.M. THE POPLAR STREET BRIDGE WASHES AWAY.

MILLS AND SHOPS CLOSE EARLY. BY NOON, WATER IS 3 TO 10 FEET DEEP IN THE STREETS. PEOPLE ARE STRANDED IN THEIR HOMES.

SOMETIME BETWEEN NOON AND 1 P.M., THE RAILROAD YARDMASTER AT EAST CONEMAUGH RECEIVES A TELEGRAPH MESSAGE: "SOUTH FORK DAM IS LIABLE TO BREAK: NOTIFY THE PEOPE OF JOHNSTOWN TO PREPARE FOR THE WORST."

THE COLLAPSE

MAY 31, 1889 – AS HEAVY RAINS RAISE THE LEVEL OF LAKE CONEMAUGH, A WORK GANG DIGS A SECOND SPILLWAY ON THE WESTERN END OF THE SOUTH FORK DAM TO RELIEVE THE PRESSURE ON THE EAST SPILLWAY.

IT WAS TOO LITTLE TOO LATE.

AT 11 A.M., COL. ELIAS J. UNGER, PRESIDENT OF THE SOUTH FORK FISHING AND HUNTING CLUB, SENDS HIS CHIEF ENGINEER, JOHN PARKE, TO WARN THE CITIZENS OF SOUTH FORK THAT THE DAM IS ABOUT TO COLLAPSE.

NOBODY BELIEVES HIM.

PARKE RETURNS TO THE DAM BY 1 P.M, ONLY TO SEE THAT THE WATER HAD ALREADY STARTED POURING OVER ITS CREST.

AT **3 O'CLOCK** A 10 FT. SECTION BREAKS LOOSE FROM THE DAM. SECONDS LATER THE ENTIRE DAM **ERUPTS,** SPEWING **20 MILLION TONS** OF WATER INTO THE CONEMAUGH VALLEY. THE JOHNSTOWN FLOOD HAD BEGUN!

MAY 31, 1889 – MINUTES AFTER THE SOUTH FORK DAM GIVES AWAY, A **40 FT. HIGH WALL OF WATER HITS**

the village of South Fork.

SINCE IT WAS BUILT ON A HILLSIDE, MOST OF THE TOWN IS SPARED.

NEVERTHELESS, 20 TO 30 BUILDINGS ARE DESTROYED AND 4 MEN DROWN.

TWO MILES DOWNSTREAM, THE FLOOD SMASHES INTO THE 75 FT. HIGH *PORTAGE RAILROAD* VIADUCT. THE BRIDGE HOLDS MOMENTARILY, FORMING ANOTHER DAM. SUDDENLY IT COLLAPSES. WATER AND DEBRIS EXPLODE INTO THE VALLEY WITH MAXIMUM POWER.

A MILE OR SO BEYOND THE VIADUCT IS THE VILLAGE OF **MINERAL POINT** WITH 30 HOUSES AND 200 PEOPLE. THE JOHNSTOWN FLOOD FLATTENS IT AND KILLS 16 RESIDENTS.

MAY 31, 1889. 3:30 PM. IT IS A HALF HOUR SINCE THE SOUTH FORK DAM COLLAPSED. A MOUNTAIN OF WATER AND DEBRIS APPROACHES A PENNSYLVANIA RAIL-ROAD WORK CREW THAT IS CLEARING A LANDSLIDE BELOW MINERAL POINT.
WHAT'S THAT ROARING NOISE?
SOUTH FORK
VIADUCT
MINERAL POINT
John Hess, THE ENGINEER, KNOWS INSTINCTIVELY:
THE LAKE'S BROKE!
THE WORK CREW SCAMPERS UP THE HILLSIDE.
HESS AND HIS FIREMAN, J.B. PLUMMER, PUT ON STEAM AND TIE DOWN THE WHISTLE.

HESS THROWS THE ENGINE INTO REVERSE AND, WITH THE FLOOD ALMOST ON TOP OF THEM, THEY RACE BACK TO EAST CONEMAUGH WHERE...

PENNSYLVANIA RR
124

THE DAY EXPRESS IS BLOCKING THE TRACKS. THEY PULL TO A STOP AND JUMP. HESS RUNS TO HIS HOME IN EAST CONEMAUGH IN TIME TO GET HIS FAMILY TO HIGHER GROUND.

MAY 31, 1889. 3:45 P.M.

The Day Express

HAS BEEN DELAYED 5 HOURS IN THE EAST CONEMAUGH RAIL YARD BECAUSE OF THE STORM. MANY PASSENGERS BELIEVE THEY WILL BE SAFE INSIDE THE TRAIN IF THE SOUTH FORK DAM BREAKS.

AS JOHN HESS'S LOCOMOTIVE BACKS INTO THE YARD WITH ITS WHISTLE BLASTING, THE *EXPRESS* CONDUCTOR REALIZES WHAT HAPPENED.

GET TO THE HILL! GET TO THE HILL!
PENNSYLVA

MOST PASSENGERS RUN FOR THEIR LIVES, BUT BETWEEN THEM & THE HIGH GROUND IS A 10 FT. WIDE DITCH WITH DEEP, RUSHING WATER. SOME HESITATE THERE; SOME JUMP.

CYRUS SCHICK OF READING AND HIS SISTER-IN-LAW FALL IN AND DROWN.

OTHERS FALL IN AND FLOUNDER. DR. GEORGE GRAHAM OF PORT ROYAL JUMPS ACROSS, THEN HELPS 8 WOMEN OUT OF THE DITCH.

ELIZABETH BRYAN OF PHILADELPHIA AND HER FRIEND, JENNIE PAULSON OF PITTSBURGH GO BACK FOR THEIR BOOTS. WHILE THEY ARE IN THE CAR, THE JOHNSTOWN FLOOD HITS.

EAST CONEMAUGH

IS THE NEXT VICTIM OF THE JOHNSTOWN FLOOD. THE WAVE HITS FRONT ST. AND 40 BUILDINGS TOPPLE LIKE DOMINOES.

IN THE RAIL YARD, THE ROUNDHOUSE IS CRUSHED AND LOCOMOTIVES WEIGHING AS MUCH AS 80 TONS ARE PICKED UP AND CARRIED BY THE FLOOD AS IF THEY ARE TOYS. THE TIME IS 3:55 PM, MAY 31, 1889.

Patrick M. Reynolds

THE ROUNDHOUSE DEFLECTS THE WAVE AWAY FROM SECTION 2 OF THE *DAY EXPRESS*. THE 16 PEOPLE INSIDE WHO DECIDED NOT TO RUN FOR IT ARE SOAKED AND SCARED, BUT ALIVE.

SECTION ONE DOES NOT FARE AS WELL. IT IS RIPPED APART; 22 ARE KILLED. NOW, AS THE TIDAL WAVE ROLLS ON, IT CARRIES TREES, TRAINS, HOUSES, & HUMAN CORPSES.

MAY 31, 1889 - 4:02 PM. PAST EAST CONE-MAUGH, THE RIVER CHANNEL STRAIGHTENS OUT. THE FLOOD PICKS UP SPEED AS IT BEARS DOWN ON THE NEXT VILLAGE, A SUBURB OF JOHNSTOWN.

WOODVALE
IS A NEW AND PROSPEROUS COMPANY TOWN, THE PRIDE OF THE CAMBRIA IRON COMPANY. ON ITS WEST SIDE STANDS THE GAUTIER WIRE WORKS.
Patrick M. Reynolds

WOODVALE IS HIT WITHOUT WARNING. THE WIRE FACTORY IS DEMOLISHED.

ITS BOILERS EXPLODE AS THE WATER ENGULFS THEM.

THE TROLLEY SHED GOES WITH 89 HORSES AND 30 TONS OF HAY. WITHIN 5 MINUTES, THE TOWN IS REDUCED TO A MUD FLAT. OF THE 1,000 RESIDENTS, 314 ARE DEAD.

IN ADDITION TO THE MOUNTAIN OF WRECKAGE, THE FLOOD NOW CARRIES MILES OF BARBED WIRE FROM WOODVALE'S WIRE WORKS AS IT ROARS INTO THE CITY OF JOHNSTOWN.

MAY 31, 1889. 4:06 PM– THE MOUNTAIN OF WATER AND DEBRIS FROM THE BROKEN *SOUTH FORK DAM* RUMBLES DOWN THE CONEMAUGH VALLEY, FORCING THE RIVER AHEAD OF IT TO BECOME
a small tidal wave.
REV. H.L. CHAPMAN LOOKS OUT HIS WINDOW ON MAIN ST. JUST AS THAT WAVE ENTERS JOHNSTOWN. TRAPPED ATOP A CAREENING BOXCAR IN THAT TORRENT IS THE B&O RAILROAD TICKET AGENT.
Patrick M. Reynolds

QUICKLY, THE AGENT GRABS A TREE BRANCH AND SWINGS ONTO THE ROOF OF CHAPMAN'S PORCH. OTHER PEOPLE HAVE ALREADY BEEN GIVEN REFUGE IN CHAPMAN'S PARSONAGE.

EVERYONE IN THE PARSONAGE FLEES TO THE ATTIC. SECONDS LATER, ANOTHER MAN DIVES THROUGH THE ATTIC WINDOW JUST AS THE MAIN WAVE HITS THE CITY. LUCKILY, THESE PEOPLE SURVIVE.

A FEW BLOCKS AWAY, HARRIET M. OGLE, THE MANAGER OF THE WESTERN UNION OFFICE, IS STRANDED ON THE SECOND FLOOR OF THE TELEGRAPH BUILDING AT WALNUT & WASHINGTON WITH HER DAUGHTER, MINNIE. SHE IS STILL TRYING TO TRANSMIT WHEN THE FLOOD HITS.
THEIR BODIES ARE NEVER IDENTIFIED.

MAY 31, 1889. 4:07 PM – VERY FEW PEOPLE SEE IT COMING, BUT EVERYONE HEARS IT, A DEEP, STEADY RUMBLE THAT GROWS LOUDER UNTIL IT ROARS LIKE THUNDER. SURVIVORS WILL LATER DESCRIBE IT AS A WALL OF WATER AND DEBRIS AT LEAST 36 FEET HIGH. ABOVE IS A CLOUD OF DARK SPRAY (FROM THE EXPLODED BOILERS AT THE IRON WORKS IN WOODVALE) WHICH WILL BE REMEMBERED AS *THE DEATH MIST.* THE YELLS AND SCREAMS OF VICTIMS ARE DROWNED OUT BY THE EAR-SPLITTING SCREECHES AND CRASHES OF **COLLAPSING BUILDINGS** AS

THE FLOOD HITS JOHNSTOWN.

GENERA
Patrick M. Reynolds

The Devastation of Johnstown

TAKES ABOUT 10 MINUTES ON THE AFTERNOON OF MAY 31, 1889.
THE FLOOD TAKES 3 MAIN ROUTES THROUGH THE CITY:

ONE FOLLOWS THE CHANNEL OF THE LITTLE CONEMAUGH ALONG THE NORTHERN SIDE OF TOWN.

ONE DRIVES DOWN THE CENTER, KNOCKING DOWN BRICK BUILDINGS ON MAIN AND LOCUST STS.

THE THIRD OBLITERATES THE EASTERN END OF THE CITY BEHIND THE METHODIST CHURCH.

ON REACHING THE FAR SIDE OF THE CITY, THE WAVE SLAMS INTO A HILL THAT RISES 550 FEET ABOVE STONY CREEK. THE HORRENDOUS BACKLASH SENDS A WAVE UP STONY CREEK WHICH DESTROYS MILES OF THE HEAVILY POPULATED VALLEY.

OTHER WAVES POUND BACK ON JOHNSTOWN, TOPPLING BUILDINGS THAT SOMEHOW SURVIVED THE FIRST ONSLAUGHT.

The Pennsylvania Railroad Bridge
CROSSES THE CONEMAUGH RIVER JUST BELOW THE POINT WHERE STONY CREEK MEETS THE LITTLE CONEMAUGH. EVENTUALLY, ALL THE WATER FROM THE JOHNSTOWN FLOOD MUST PASS THIS BRIDGE.

AFTER STRIKING THE HILL ABOVE STONY CREEK, THE MAIN WAVE OF THE FLOOD BREAKS APART, SO THE BRIDGE IS NOT HIT BY THE FULL FORCE OF THE DELUGE. CONSEQUENTLY, IT REMAINS STANDING AND DEBRIS BEGINS TO PILE UP AGAINST ITS MASSIVE STONE ARCHES.
HOUSES, BOXCARS, TREES, POLES, DEAD ANIMALS, AND HUNDREDS OF PEOPLE-DEAD AND ALIVE-ARE DRIVEN AGAINST THE BRIDGE, FORMING A MOUNTAIN HIGHER THAN THE BRIDGE ITSELF.
Patrick M. Reynolds
THIS NEW "DAM" DOES NOT COLLAPSE AS THE VIADUCT UPSTREAM DID, BUT IT WILL CAUSE ANOTHER NIGHTMARE... FIRE!

THE FIRE AT THE BRIDGE

MAY 31, 1889. 6 P.M.–THE JOHNSTOWN FLOOD IMPRISONS SCORES OF PEOPLE IN THE DEBRIS AT THE RAILROAD BRIDGE. MANY ARE HOPELESSLY TANGLED IN THE WIRE FROM THE WOODVALE WIRE FACTORY.

SOME BELIEVE THAT OIL FROM A RAILROAD CAR SEEPED DOWN THROUGH THE MASS ONTO HOT COAL STOVES INSIDE THE MANGLED HOUSES CAUGH IN THE JAM.

AT ANY RATE, A FIRE STARTS AND QUICKLY SPREADS...

RESCUERS ARE DRIVEN BACK BY THE INTENSE HEAT AS THE MONSTROUS HEAP– 40 FEET HIGH COVERING 45 ACRES– BECOMES A FUNERAL PYRE FOR ABOUT 80 PEOPLE TRAPPED INSIDE. THE FLOOD IS OVER, BUT THE FIRE BURNS 2 MORE DAYS.

PatrickM
Reynolds

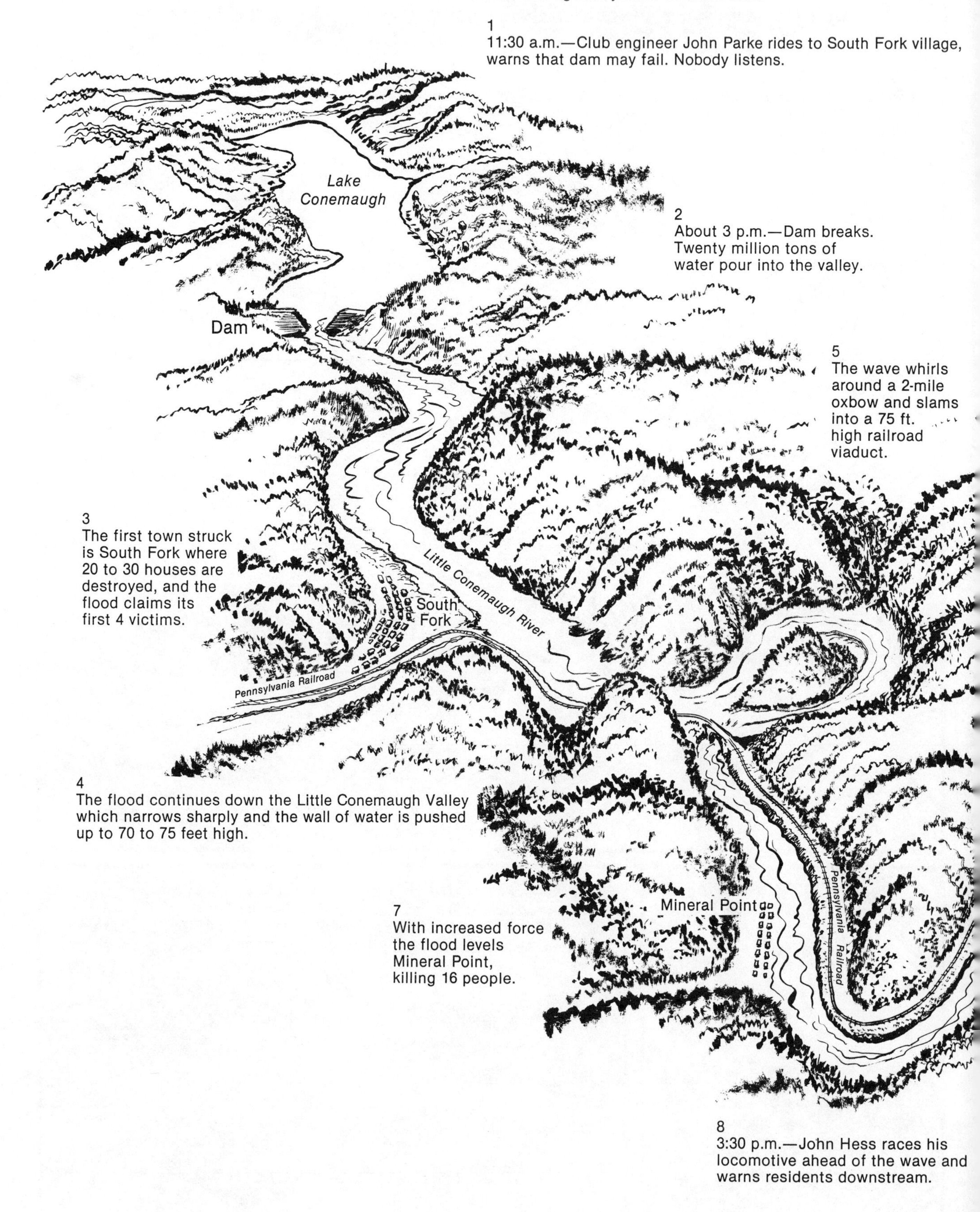
All morning heavy rains threaten dam.
1
11:30 a.m.—Club engineer John Parke rides to South Fork village, warns that dam may fail. Nobody listens.
Lake Conemaugh
2
About 3 p.m.—Dam breaks. Twenty million tons of water pour into the valley.
Dam
5
The wave whirls around a 2-mile oxbow and slams into a 75 ft. high railroad viaduct.
3
The first town struck is South Fork where 20 to 30 houses are destroyed, and the flood claims its first 4 victims.
Little Conemaugh River
South Fork
Pennsylvania Railroad
4
The flood continues down the Little Conemaugh Valley which narrows sharply and the wall of water is pushed up to 70 to 75 feet high.
Mineral Point
Pennsylvania Railroad
7
With increased force the flood levels Mineral Point, killing 16 people.
8
3:30 p.m.—John Hess races his locomotive ahead of the wave and warns residents downstream.

Sketched from a model in the Johnstown Flood Museum, this aerial view shows the sequence of the Johnstown Flood on May 31, 1889.

E
S
W
N

6

The viaduct holds for a few minutes, then collapses. Now the flood continues with renewed force.

11
4:07 p.m.—A 36 ft. high wall of water and debris rumbles into Johnstown.

12
The wave slams into a hill on the far side of the city. Part washes back on Johnstown; another part rushes up Stony Creek valley.

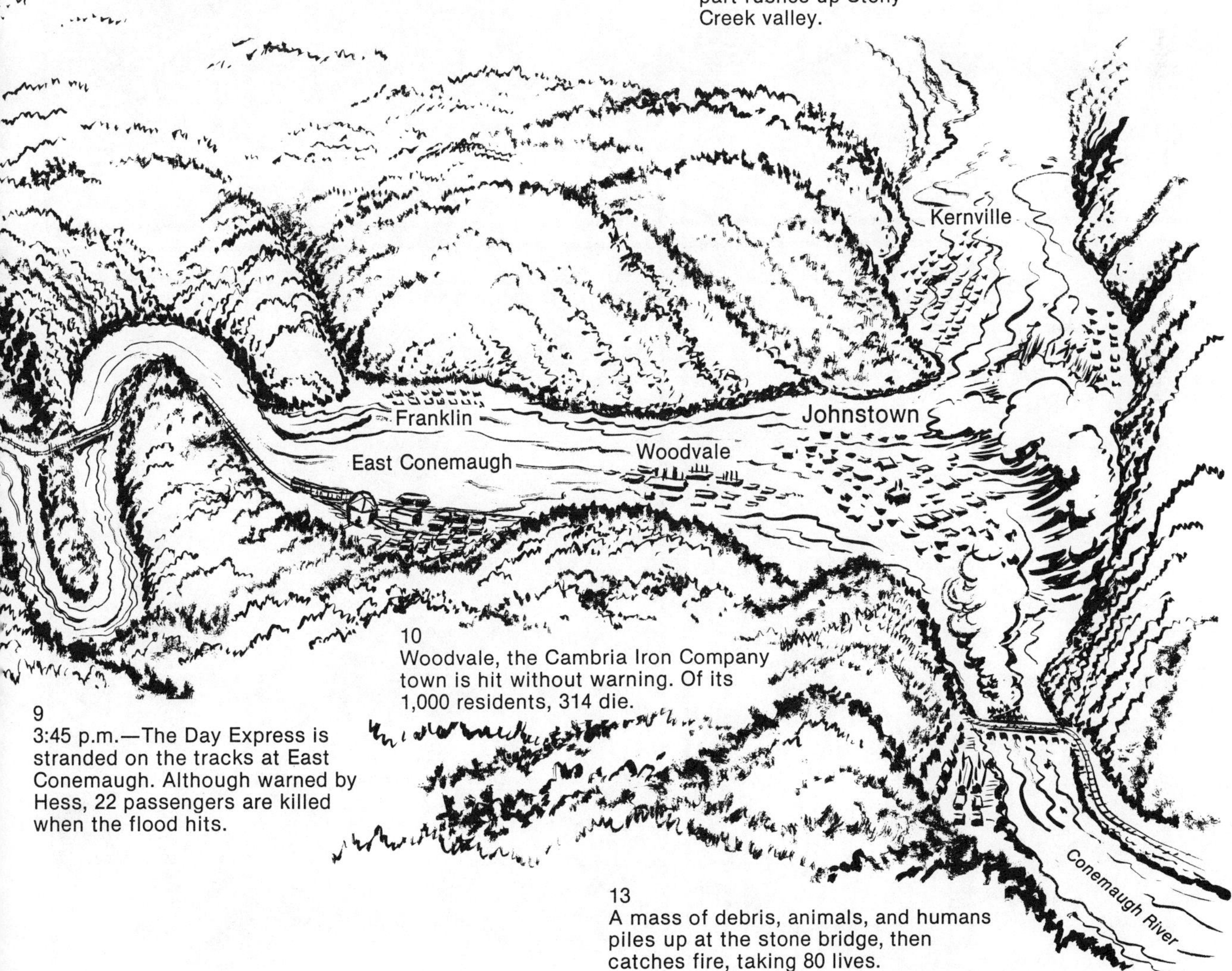
Kernville
Franklin
Johnstown
Woodvale
East Conemaugh
Conemaugh River

10
Woodvale, the Cambria Iron Company town is hit without warning. Of its 1,000 residents, 314 die.

9
3:45 p.m.—The Day Express is stranded on the tracks at East Conemaugh. Although warned by Hess, 22 passengers are killed when the flood hits.

13
A mass of debris, animals, and humans piles up at the stone bridge, then catches fire, taking 80 lives.

SURVIVORS
OF THE JOHNSTOWN FLOOD HUDDLE THROUGHOUT THE NIGHT OF MAY 31, 1889 ON GREEN HILL, PROSPECT HILL, AND ON THE SLOPES ABOVE KERNVILLE, CAMBRIA CITY, AND WOODVALE. MOST ARE INJURED, HUNGRY, AND CHILLED TO THE BONE.

DURING THE NIGHT, THE WATER RECEDES.
AT DAWN, PEOPLE BEGIN TO SEARCH FOR THEIR HOMES AND RELATIVES.
THE AIR REEKS OF SMOKE, SLUDGE, AND DEATH.

ONE MAN WRITES, "PEOPLE WHO HAD HARDLY KNOWN EACH OTHER BEFORE THE FLOOD EMBRACED... WHILE THOSE WHO FOUND RELATIONS RUSHED INTO EACH OTHER'S ARMS AND CRIED."

BY NOON, RESCUE TEAMS ARE BRINGING PEOPLE DOWN FROM TREES AND ROOFTOPS. OTHERS SEARCH AMONG THE WRECKAGE FOR SIGNS OF LIFE. *NINETY-NINE ENTIRE FAMILIES HAD BEEN WIPED OUT.*
Patrick M. Reynolds

JUNE 1, 1889- THE DAY AFTER THE JOHNSTOWN FLOOD, ALL ABLE-BODIED MEN ATTEND A MEETING AT THE ADAMS STREET SCHOOLHOUSE TO ORGANIZE THE
RECOVERY EFFORT.
ARTHUR J. MOXHAM, OWNER OF A FOUNDRY THAT MAKES RAILS FOR TROLLEYS IS ELECTED "DICTATOR." HE QUICKLY FORMS COMMITTEES TO TACKLE THE MOST PRESSING PROBLEMS.

MOXHAM PUTS HIS BUSINESS PARTNER, TOM JOHNSON, AND CHARLES ZIMMERMAN IN CHARGE OF REMOVING DEAD ANIMALS AND WRECKAGE.

THE REVERENDS BEALE AND CHAPMAN SET UP MORGUES FOR WHAT WILL AMOUNT TO 2,209 DEAD. ONE OUT OF 3 BODIES ARE NEVER IDENTIFIED.

CAPTAIN A.N. HART IS PLACED IN CHARGE OF THE POLICE FORCE. HE DEPUTIZES 75 MEN, MOST FROM MOXHAM'S FACTORY, WHO CUT TIN STARS FROM TOMATO CANS FOUND IN THE RUBBLE.

THEY CORDON OFF THE FIRST NATIONAL BANK AND THE DIBERT BANK, THEN RECOVER $6,000 IN CASH FROM TRUNKS AND BUREAUS LYING AROUND.
Patrick M Reynolds

THE ADJUTANT GENERAL
OF PENNSYLVANIA IN 1889 WAS A POLITICIAN WITH MEAGER MILITARY EXPERIENCE—
DANIEL HARTMAN HASTINGS.
AS SOON AS HE HEARS ABOUT THE JOHNSTOWN FLOOD, HASTINGS LEAVES HIS HOME IN BELLEFONTE AND RIDES NON-STOP TO THE STRICKEN CITY. THE 70-MILE TRIP TAKES A FULL DAY.

AS DAWN BREAKS ON JUNE 2, 1889 HASTINGS OBSERVES WORK CREWS ARRIVING BY THE TRAINLOAD, ALONG WITH A CAR FULL OF COFFINS & 50 UNDERTAKERS FROM PITTSBURGH.

2058
NIA RAILROAD
JOHNSTOWN

THE SITUATION BECOMES TOO MUCH FOR MOXHAM'S COMMITTEES TO HANDLE. BY NIGHTFALL THEY ASK GOVERNOR BEAVER TO SEND THE NATIONAL GUARD TO JOHNSTOWN.

HASTINGS TAKES COMMAND WHEN THE TROOPS ARRIVE. ALL IN ALL, *THE GUARD* DOES A FINE JOB KEEPING ORDER. ONE MEASURE THAT HASTINGS TAKES TO PREVENT TROUBLE IS TO BAN THE SALE OF LIQUOR IN THE AREA DURING THE RECOVERY.

Patrick M. Reynolds

DR. JOHN LOWMAN AND DR. WILLIAM MATTHEWS ARE RESPONSIBLE FOR OPENING TEMPORARY HOSPITALS IN JOHNSTOWN THE DAY AFTER THE FLOOD. BUT THERE IS HARDLY ANY MEDICINE.

HELP ARRIVES FROM WASHINGTON, D.C. ON WEDNESDAY MORNING, JUNE 5, 1889. SHE IS A LITTLE, 67 YEAR-OLD SPINSTER NAMED
Clara Barton.

WITH HER ARE SOME 50 DOCTORS AND NURSES, PART OF THE NEW
AMERICAN RED CROSS.
FROM HER HEADQUARTERS ON PROSPECT HILL, MISS BARTON WORKS ALMOST ROUND THE CLOCK, DIRECTING HUNDREDS OF VOLUNTEERS WHO DISTRIBUTE NEARLY
$½ MILLION
WORTH OF FOOD, CLOTHING, BLANKETS, AND CASH.
RED CROSS
RED CROSS
Patrick M. Reynolds

SHE ALSO SETS UP 6 HOSTELS AND SEVERAL HOSPITAL TENTS.

ON HER RETURN TO WASHINGTON, PRESIDENT AND MRS. BENJAMIN HARRISON HONOR HER WITH A DINNER. *THE RED CROSS HAD PASSED ITS FIRST REAL TEST.*

The Trouble With Tourists...

WITHIN THREE DAYS AFTER THE FLOOD, JOHNSTOWN IS CRAWLING WITH EDITORS, REPORTERS, AND ARTISTS. THEIR STORIES ATTRACT HUNDREDS OF SIGHTSEERS...

WHO GET IN EVERYBODY'S WAY. MANY ARRIVE ON EXCURSION TRAINS IN THEIR SUNDAY CLOTHES WITH PICNIC BASKETS AND A NEW INVENTION–THE *BROWNIE* CAMERA.

THE MOST POPULAR PICTURE-TAKING SITE IS THE HOME OF JOHN SCHULTZ AT MAIN AND UNION STREETS.
SIX PEOPLE WERE IN THIS HOUSE WHEN THE FLOOD HIT. THEY ALL SURVIVED.
Patrick M. Reynolds

IT TAKES GENERAL HASTINGS ONE MONTH TO CONVINCE THE RAILROADS TO STOP SELLING TICKETS TO ANYONE HAVING NO BUSINESS IN JOHNSTOWN. THAT ENDED THE TOURIST PROBLEM.

THE GREATEST OUTPOURING OF CHARITY

THE COUNTRY HAS EVER KNOWN IS GENERATED BY NEWS STORIES OF THE JOHNSTOWN FLOOD.

SCHOOL CHILDREN CONTRIBUTE NICKELS & DIMES.

FLOOD
FUN

JOHN PHILIP **SOUSA** GIVES A BENEFIT BAND CONCERT IN WASHINGTON.

BUFFALO BILL HOLDS A SPECIAL WILD WEST SHOW IN PARIS, FRANCE.

A SOUTHERN CIVIL WAR VETERAN SENDS FOUR $100 CONFEDERATE BILLS.

DONATIONS FROM EVERY STATE AND 14 COUNTRIES AMOUNT TO **$3,742,818.78.** MINNEAPOLIS SENDS 16 CARLOADS OF FLOUR. CINCINNATI GIVES 10 TONS OF HAM.

R.R.
CAPACITY
XXX

A DEMOLITIONS EXPERT ARRIVES WITH A SHIPMENT OF DYNAMITE TO BREAK THE JAM AT THE BRIDGE. FOR DAYS THE VALLEY ECHOES WITH EXPLOSIONS UNTIL THE DEBRIS IS CLEARED.

WILLIAM FLINN OF THE BOOTH & FLINN CONSTRUCTION CO., PITTSBURGH CONTRIBUTES 1,100 CARPENTERS AND LABORERS.

THE HOMELESS ARE SHELTERED IN PREFABRICATED "OKLAHOMA" HOUSES. BY MIDSUMMER, 1889, JOHNSTOWN LOOKS LIKE A CROSS BETWEEN AN ARMY CAMP AND A WILD WEST TOWN.

Patrick M. Reynolds

Life Goes On
SUNDAY, JUNE 9, 1889–THE SUN SHINES OVER JOHNSTOWN FOR THE FIRST TIME SINCE THE FLOOD, TEN DAYS EARLIER.
ON THE EMBANKMENT ABOVE THE RAIL DEPOT, NEAR GENERAL HASTING'S HEADQUARTERS, THE CHAPLAIN OF THE 14th REGIMENT AND THE REVERENDS H.C. CHAPMAN AND DAVID BEALE CONDUCT THE FIRST SERVICES SINCE THE FLOOD.
. . . BY GOD'S GRACE, WE SHALL MAKE THE CITY MORE THRIVING THAN EVER!

THREE BABIES BORN IN JOHNSTOWN ON THE DAY OF THE FLOOD **WILL GO** THROUGH LIFE WITH THE NAMES MOSES WILLIAM, FLOOD RAYMOND, AND FLOOD RHODES.

IN TIME, STORIES OF THE FLOOD **WILL SOUND LIKE** LEGENDS. VAUDEVILLE COMICS COIN THE PHRASE

THE DAM'S BUSTED. HEAD FOR THE HILLS!

SIGNS LIKE THIS APPEAR IN SALOONS THROUGHOUT THE COUNTRY.
DON'T SPIT ON THE FLOOR REMEMBER THE JOHNSTOWN FLOOD

WILLIAM FLINN **WILL BECOME** A STATE SENATOR AND BOSS OF THE REPUBLICAN PARTY IN PITTSBURGH. EVERY ELECTION HE **WILL REMIND THE VOTERS ABOUT HOW** HIS CONSTRUCTION COMPANY HELPED REBUILD JOHNSTOWN.

AND GENERAL DAN HASTINGS **WILL RIDE** THE NAME HE MADE FOR HIMSELF AT JOHNSTOWN INTO THE GOVERNOR'S OFFICE IN 1895.

Fixing the Blame
THE DAM WHICH BURST ON MAY 31, 1889 CAUSING THE JOHNSTOWN FLOOD WAS OWNED BY THE SOUTH FORK FISHING AND HUNTING CLUB. THREE NIGHTS LATER, AN ANGRY MOB GOES TO THE CLUB LOOKING FOR MEMBERS.

FINDING NONE, THEY BREAK INTO THE CLUB MEMBERS' ELEGANT COTTAGES AND TRASH THEM.

A CORONER'S INQUEST IS HELD ON JUNE 6 IN CAMBRIA COUNTY COURT TO DETERMINE THE CAUSE OF DEATH OF ONE FLOOD VICTIM, MRS. ELLEN HITE.

THE VERDICT IS
DEATH BY DROWNING, CAUSED BY THE BREAKING OF THE SOUTH FORK DAM.

BUT THE JURY ADDED
...THE OWNERS OF SAID DAM ARE RESPONSIBLE FOR THE FEARFUL LOSS OF LIFE AND PROPERTY.

MEANWHILE, THE EDITORS OF TWO ENGINEERING MAGAZINES INVESTIGATE THE DAM, THEN LEAK THEIR FINDINGS TO THE PRESS. THE JUNE 9 HEADLINE OF THE N.Y. TIMES READS, "AN ENGINEERING CRIME – THE DAM OF INFERIOR CONSTRUCTION."
THIS BRINGS ON A RASH OF LAWSUITS THAT WILL DRAG ON FOR YEARS.
Patrick M. Reynolds

"A Visitation Of Providence"

EARLY IN AUGUST, 1889, A GROUP OF JOHNSTOWN BUSINESSMEN SUE THE SOUTH FORK FISHING & HUNTING CLUB FOR THE DEATH AND DESTRUCTION CAUSED BY THE COLLAPSE OF THE CLUB'S DAM ON MAY 31st.

MEANWHILE, REPORTERS IN PITTSBURGH EXAMINE THE CLUB'S FINANCES AND LEARN THAT, DESPITE THE COLOSSAL WEALTH OF ITS MEMBERS, THE CLUB IS VIRTUALLY BROKE.

THE LAWSUITS ARE TRIED IN PITTSBURGH. THE CLUB'S ATTORNEYS PLEAD NOT GUILTY, CLAIMING THAT THE JOHNSTOWN FLOOD HAD BEEN "A VISITATION OF PROVIDENCE."

THE COURT AGREES AND FINDS THE SOUTH FORK CLUB NOT GUILTY.

THE FINAL ACT OF THE JOHNSTOWN FLOOD TAKES PLACE ON JUNE 1, 1892 WHEN A MONUMENT TO THE UNKNOWN DEAD IS UNVEILED IN GRANDVIEW CEMETERY. BEHIND IT ARE THE GRAVES OF 663 UNIDENTIFIED VICTIMS.
Patrick M. Reynolds
IN THE END, NOT A CENT IS EVER COLLECTED THROUGH DAMAGE SUITS FROM THE CLUB NOR ANY OF ITS MEMBERS.

DANIEL H. HASTINGS WAS BORN FEB. 26, 1849 IN LAMAR TOWNSHIP, CLINTON COUNTY. AS THE YOUNGEST OF 9 CHILDREN, HE LEARNED EARLY THE VALUE OF A LOUD, CLEAR VOICE.

HIS SPEECH NOMINATING SEN. JOHN SHERMAN FOR PRESIDENT AT THE 1888 REPUBLICAN CONVENTION EARNED HASTINGS NATIONAL FAME AS

a Spellbinding Orator.

HASTINGS' ELECTION TO THE GOVERNORSHIP IN 1894 USHERED IN THE GOLDEN AGE OF REPUBLICANISM IN PENNSYLVANIA. FOR THE NEXT 40 YEARS, UNTIL 1935, THE COMMONWEALTH HAD 10 REPUBLICAN GOVERNORS.

DURING HASTINGS' TERM, EDUCATION WAS MADE COMPULSORY FOR CHILDREN BETWEEN THE AGES OF 8 AND 13. FREE TRANSPORTATION TO SCHOOL WAS MANDATED IN 1897.

THE STATE'S DEPARTMENT OF AGRICULTURE WAS STARTED IN 1895.

THE GAME COMMISSION WAS ESTABLISHED THAT SAME YEAR.

HUNTING LICENCE

AND, WHILE HASTINGS WAS GOV., THE CAPITOL BUILDING BURNED TO THE GROUND ON FEB. 2, 1897.

HASTINGS DIED AT HOME IN BELLEFONTE ONLY 4 YEARS AFTER LEAVING OFFICE. HE WAS 53.

Fort Augusta,
AT PRESENT-DAY SUNBURY, WAS THE LARGEST FORT IN PENNSYLVANIA DURING THE FRENCH AND INDIAN WAR-EVEN BIGGER THAN THE FRENCH FORT, DUQUESNE, IN WHAT IS NOW PITTSBURGH.
CONSTRUCTED OF LOGS IN 1756, FORT AUGUSTA WAS 204 FT. ACROSS WITH A MOAT, AN OUTER STOCKADE, 4 BLOCK-HOUSES, AND A COVERED WALKWAY TO THE SUSQUEHANNA RIVER.
A REGIMENT (8 COMPANIES OF 50 MEN EACH) WAS GARRISONED THERE.
Patrick M Reynolds
THE FORT WAS PRESUMABLY NAMED AFTER PRINCESS AUGUSTA, WIDOW OF THE PRINCE OF WALES & MOTHER OF THE FUTURE MONARCH, THE NOTORIOUS GEORGE III.
FORT AUGUSTA BECAME A CENTER OF PEACEFUL INDIAN ACTIVITY, PROVIDING A BASE FOR SENDING ENVOYS TO CONFER WITH THE INDIANS, AND A REST STOP FOR INDIANS THEMSELVES ON THEIR WAY TO PEACE TALKS. TRADE WITH THE INDIANS WAS ENHANCED WITH A TRADING POST INSIDE THE FORT.

JOHN WRIGHT,
A QUAKER FROM CHESTER, CAME TO THE SUSQUEHANNA VALLEY IN 1724 TO PREACH THE GOSPEL TO THE INDIANS.

HE LIKED THE SHAWNEE TOWN OF **SHAWANNAH** SO MUCH THAT HE STAYED.

FIVE YEARS LATER HE STARTED TO RUN A FERRY ACROSS THE SUSQUEHANNA AND CHANGED THE NAME OF THE PLACE TO WRIGHT'S FERRY, LANCASTER COUNTY. WRIGHT GOT RICH AND AMASSED A LOT OF PROPERTY.
Patrick M. Reynolds

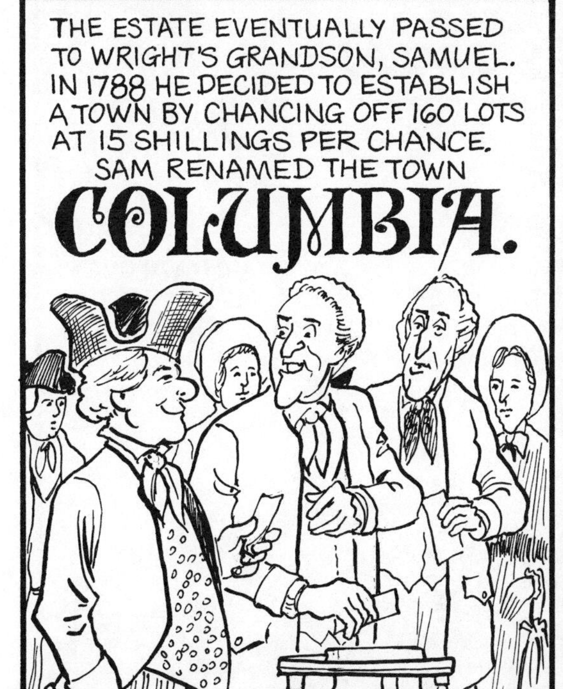
THE ESTATE EVENTUALLY PASSED TO WRIGHT'S GRANDSON, SAMUEL. IN 1788 HE DECIDED TO ESTABLISH A TOWN BY CHANCING OFF 160 LOTS AT 15 SHILLINGS PER CHANCE.
SAM RENAMED THE TOWN
COLUMBIA.

A BRIDGE REPLACED THE FERRY IN 1814. BY THE MID 19th CENTURY COLUMBIA WAS **INTERSECTED** BY A CANAL, RAILROAD, AND MAJOR HIGHWAY. CONSEQUENTLY, IT WAS ONE OF THE BUSIEST AND WILDEST TOWNS IN THE EAST.
IN THE 1790's CONGRESS ALMOST SELECTED COLUMBIA AS THE SITE FOR THE NATION'S CAPITAL.

JEFFERSON COUNTY
WAS ORGANIZED IN 1804 AND NAMED AFTER THE PRESIDENT OF THE U.S. AT THE TIME.
MOST OF THE EARLIEST SETTLERS WERE VETERANS OF THE REVOLUTIONARY WAR. WOLVES WERE SO NUMEROUS AND BOLD THAT THEY WOULD COME WITHIN A FEW YARDS OF CABINS AT NIGHT AND HOWL.
SIGEL
BROCKWAY
BROOKVILLE
POINT BARNETT
REYNOLDSVILLE
PUNXSUTAWNEY
THE FIRST SETTLERS WERE JOSEPH BARNETT FROM LINGLESTOWN; HIS BROTHER, ANDREW, AND HIS BROTHER-IN-LAW, SAMUEL SCOTT. WITH THE HELP OF SOME SENECA INDIANS, THEY ERECTED A SAW MILL IN 1797 AND FOUNDED A TOWN CALLED PORT BARNETT.
AROUND 1812-1820, A MUNCY INDIAN KNOWN AS OLD CAPTAIN HUNT HAD HIS CAMP ON RED BANK, NOW PART OF BROOKVILLE, THE COUNTY SEAT. MAKING HIS LIVING AS A HUNTER, HE ONCE KILLED 78 BEARS IN ONE YEAR. JEFFERSON COUNTY IS STILL A GREAT PLACE FOR HUNTING AND FISHING.
THE COUNTY'S GROWTH MUSHROOMED AFTER 1830 WHEN LUMBERMEN FROM NEW ENGLAND AND NEW YORK BOUGHT VAST TRACTS OF LAND. FOR MANY YEARS SOME OF THE LARGEST TIMBERING OPERATIONS IN THE STATE WERE CENTERED IN THE COUNTY.
BITUMINOUS COAL MINING TOOK OVER AS THE AREA'S MAJOR INDUSTRY DURING THE FIRST HALF OF THE 20th CENTURY.
Patrick M. Reynolds

PIKE COUNTY
WAS CREATED IN 1814 AND NAMED FOR COL. ZEBULON M. PIKE, A HERO OF THE WAR OF 1812 & EXPLORER WHO DISCOVERED PIKE'S PEAK IN COLORADO.
NEW YORK
LACKAWAXEN
LAKE WALLENPAUPACK
GREELEY
MATAMORAS
PROMISED LAND STATE PARK
Milford
GEO. W. CHILDS STATE PARK
DINGMAN'S FERRY
NEW JERSEY

IT IS SAID THAT THE FIRST EUROPEAN SETTLEMENT IN PENNSYLVANIA WAS THE FERTILE BOTTOM LAND NEAR MILFORD, THE COUNTY SEAT. HERE, DUTCH COLONISTS FROM NEW YORK BUILT THEIR HOMES AROUND 1660.

TO STOP INDIAN RAIDS IN THE AREA IN THE MID 1700'S, BENJAMIN FRANKLIN PUT CPT. VAN ETTEN IN CHARGE OF 39 VOLUNTEERS IN PIKE COUNTY AND OFFERED $40 FOR EACH SCALP OF AN INDIAN BRAVE.

PENNSYLVANIA AND CONNECTICUT BOTH CLAIMED PIKE COUNTY, WHICH GAVE RISE TO THE PENNAMITE WARS IN THE LATE 1700'S. IT TOOK 30 YEARS OF INTERMITTENT WARFARE UNTIL PENNSYLVANIA TOOK UNDISPUTED CONTROL OF THIS PART OF THE STATE.

Patrick M. Reynolds

A RELIGIOUS GROUP, THE SHAKERS CAME HERE TO GET RICH, BUT WERE SOON DISILLUSIONED. SARCASTICALLY, THEY CALLED THE PLACE "PROMISED LAND." IN 1903, THE STATE DESIGNATED 2,300 ACRES OF THE SAME AREA AS *PROMISED LAND STATE PARK.*

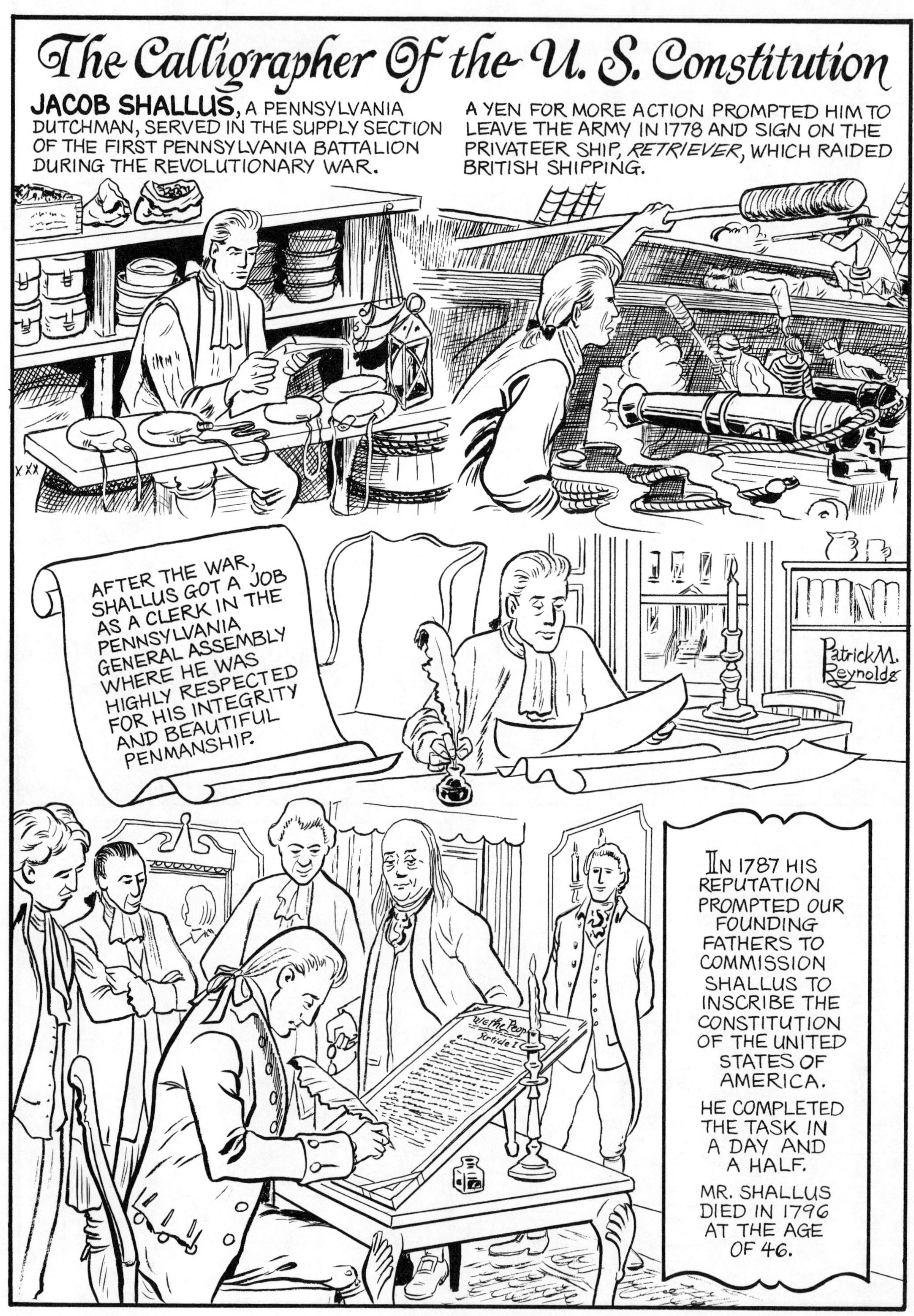
The Calligrapher Of the U. S. Constitution
JACOB SHALLUS, A PENNSYLVANIA DUTCHMAN, SERVED IN THE SUPPLY SECTION OF THE FIRST PENNSYLVANIA BATTALION DURING THE REVOLUTIONARY WAR.
A YEN FOR MORE ACTION PROMPTED HIM TO LEAVE THE ARMY IN 1778 AND SIGN ON THE PRIVATEER SHIP, RETRIEVER, WHICH RAIDED BRITISH SHIPPING.
AFTER THE WAR, SHALLUS GOT A JOB AS A CLERK IN THE PENNSYLVANIA GENERAL ASSEMBLY WHERE HE WAS HIGHLY RESPECTED FOR HIS INTEGRITY AND BEAUTIFUL PENMANSHIP.
Patrick M. Reynolds
We the People
Article I
IN 1787 HIS REPUTATION PROMPTED OUR FOUNDING FATHERS TO COMMISSION SHALLUS TO INSCRIBE THE CONSTITUTION OF THE UNITED STATES OF AMERICA.
HE COMPLETED THE TASK IN A DAY AND A HALF.
MR. SHALLUS DIED IN 1796 AT THE AGE OF 46.

America's First Volunteer Fire Company
In December, 1733, Benjamin Franklin wrote an article in his "Pennsylvania Gazette" suggesting Philadelphia organize a club or society to fight fires, similar to one in Boston.
Patrick M. Reynolds
On December 7, 1736, Franklin and 4 of his rich and powerful cronies — Isaac Paschal, William Rawle, Samuel Powell, and Philip Syng — started the Union Fire Company, the first volunteer fire company in America.
Membership was limited to 30 "men of property." Each man had to buy 6 leather buckets and 2 strong linen bags (to salvage valuables from a burning house).
UNION
UNION
UNION
The Union held supper meetings 8 times a year, usually at Widow Pratt's Sign of the Royal Standard on Market Street.
The tab was 8 shillings per member.

The Housing Ceremony

SOON AFTER BEN FRANKLIN ORGANIZED THE UNION FIRE CO. IN PHILADELPHIA, VOLUNTEER FIRE COMPANIES BEGAN TO EMERGE THROUGHOUT PENNSYLVANIA.

LANCASTER STARTED ITS FIRST COMPANY IN 1760 AND ALSO CALLED IT THE UNION. READING & YORK FORMED VOLUNTEER FIRE UNITS IN 1771. LEBANON FOLLOWED IN 1773.

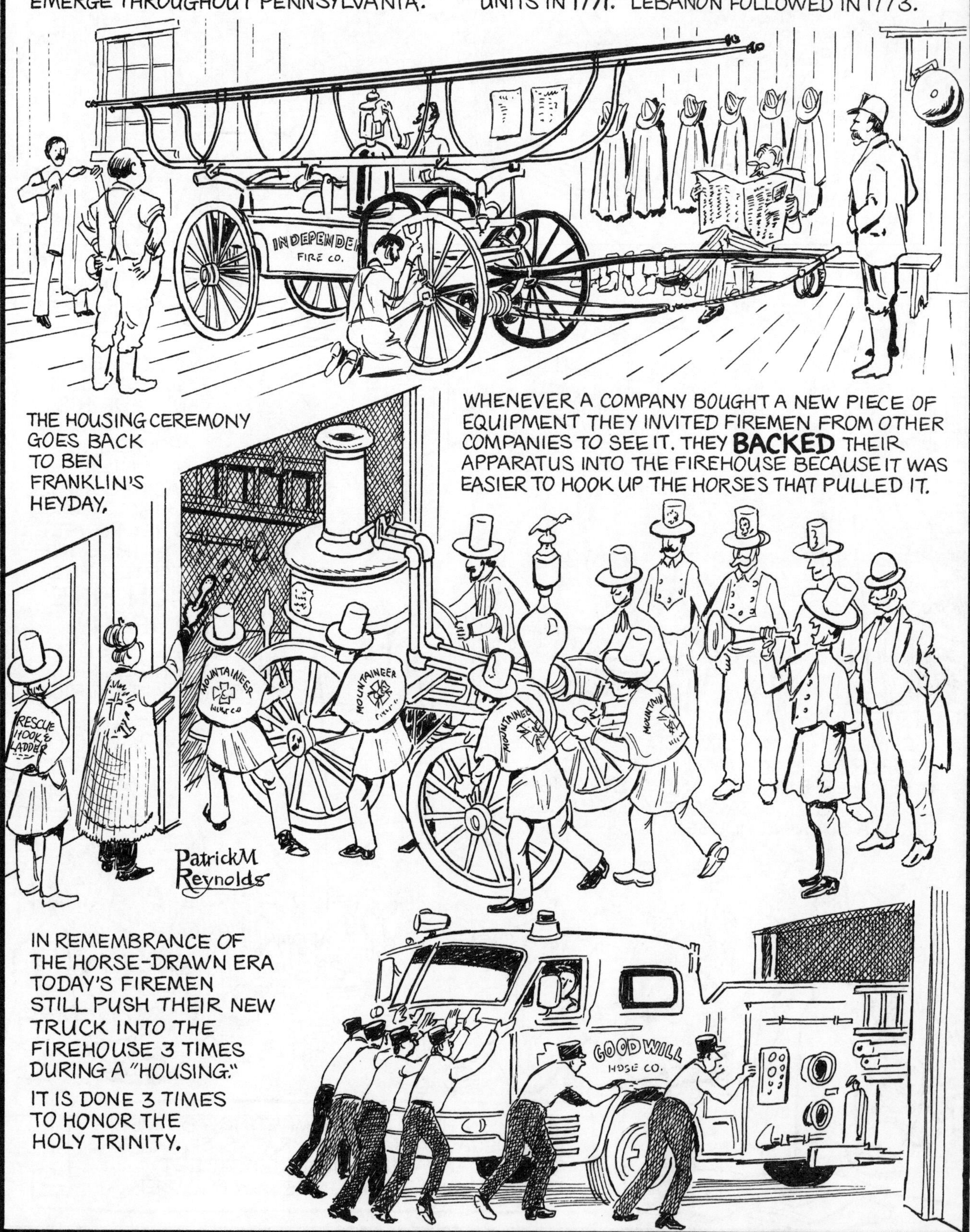
INDEPENDEN
FIRE CO.
THE HOUSING CEREMONY GOES BACK TO BEN FRANKLIN'S HEYDAY.
WHENEVER A COMPANY BOUGHT A NEW PIECE OF EQUIPMENT THEY INVITED FIREMEN FROM OTHER COMPANIES TO SEE IT. THEY BACKED THEIR APPARATUS INTO THE FIREHOUSE BECAUSE IT WAS EASIER TO HOOK UP THE HORSES THAT PULLED IT.
RESCUE HOOK & LADDER
MOUNTAINEER HOSE CO
MOUNTAINEER
PatrickM Reynolds
IN REMEMBRANCE OF THE HORSE-DRAWN ERA TODAY'S FIREMEN STILL PUSH THEIR NEW TRUCK INTO THE FIREHOUSE 3 TIMES DURING A "HOUSING."
IT IS DONE 3 TIMES TO HONOR THE HOLY TRINITY.
GOODWILL HOSE CO.

Penn-Dutch Portrait Painters

DURING THE EARLY HALF OF THE 19th CENTURY, FARMERS AND SMALL TOWN BUSINESSMEN HAD THEIR LIKENESSES PRESERVED FOR POSTERITY BY SELF-TAUGHT ARTISTS WHO ROAMED THE COUNTRYSIDE. THE ARTIST KEPT A SUPPLY OF CANVASES WITH THE FIGURES ALREADY PAINTED, THEN HE ADDED THE FACES DURING A BRIEF SITTING.

Patrick M. Reynolds

THE IDENTITIES OF MOST OF THESE FREE-SPIRITED PAINTERS IS UNKNOWN, EXCEPT FOR SAM STETINIUS, A GERMAN WHO SETTLED IN HANOVER IN 1791.

STETINIUS BECAME SO SUCCESSFUL THAT HIS STUDENTS AND IMITATORS PROSPERED FOR OVER 50 YEARS, UNTIL PHOTOGRAPHY CAME INTO VOGUE.

THEIR PAINTINGS ARE NOW VALUABLE PIECES OF AMERICAN FOLK ART. HOWEVER, THESE PENNSYLVANIA DUTCH ARTISTS CREATED THEIR MASTERPIECES IN EXCHANGE FOR A NIGHT'S LODGING, A JUG OF WHISKEY, OR FIVE DOLLARS.

CANVASES SHOWN HERE: TOP - MR. & MRS. BOMBERGER; LOWER LEFT - CHRISTIAN BUCHER, A PHARMACIST IN SCHAEFFERSTOWN; LOWER RIGHT - JENNIE HINKLE OF HANOVER.

AN ACTOR
NAMED JOHN WILKES BOOTH CAME TO FRANKLIN, VENANGO COUNTY, IN THE SPRING OF 1864. HE FOUNDED THE DRAMATIC OIL CO. WITH GEORGE ELLSLER, MANAGER OF THE CLEVELAND ACADEMY OF MUSIC, AND THOMAS Y. MEARS.

THEY DRILLED 3 WELLS ON A 60 ACRE LEASE IN CRANBERRY TOWNSHIP ALONG THE ALLEGHENY RIVER, WHICH PRODUCED 20 BARRELS A DAY. HOWEVER, IN THEIR ATTEMPT TO BOOST THE YIELD, THEY RUINED THE WELLS IN SOME MYSTERIOUS WAY.
Patrick M. Reynolds

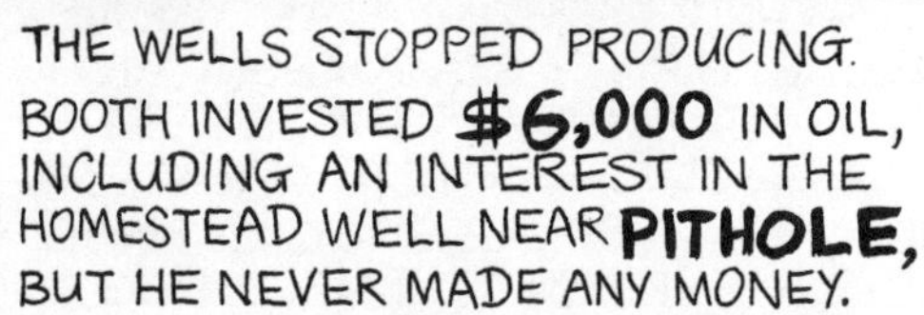
THE WELLS STOPPED PRODUCING. BOOTH INVESTED $6,000 IN OIL, INCLUDING AN INTEREST IN THE HOMESTEAD WELL NEAR PITHOLE, BUT HE NEVER MADE ANY MONEY.

ON SEPT. 27th, THE ACTOR CLOSED OUT HIS HOLDINGS IN VENANGO COUNTY AND LEFT THE AREA FOR GOOD. BOOTH WAS VIRTUALLY FORGOTTEN IN PENNSYLVANIA UNTIL...

APRIL 14, 1865, THE NIGHT HE ASSASSINATED PRESIDENT LINCOLN AT FORD'S THEATER IN WASHINGTON, DC.

Winemaking

IN THE COMMONWEALTH DATES BACK TO 1684 WHEN **WILLIAM PENN** BROUGHT SPANISH AND FRENCH VINES TO AMERICA AND PLANTED HIS OWN VINEYARD IN WHAT IS NOW **FAIRMOUNT PARK,** PHILADELPHIA.

A LITTLE OVER A CENTURY LATER THE **FIRST COMMERCIAL VINEYARD** IN THIS COUNTRY WAS ESTABLISHED BY PIERRE LEGAUX IN 1793 AT SPRING MILL NEAR **CONSHOHOCKEN.**

Patrick M. Reynolds

WINEMAKING CAME TO **ERIE COUNTY** IN 1850 WHEN MESSRS. HAMMOND & GRIFFITH PLANTED GRAPES IN **NORTH EAST** TOWNSHIP. THEY ORGANIZED THE SOUTH SHORE WINE COMPANY IN 1869.

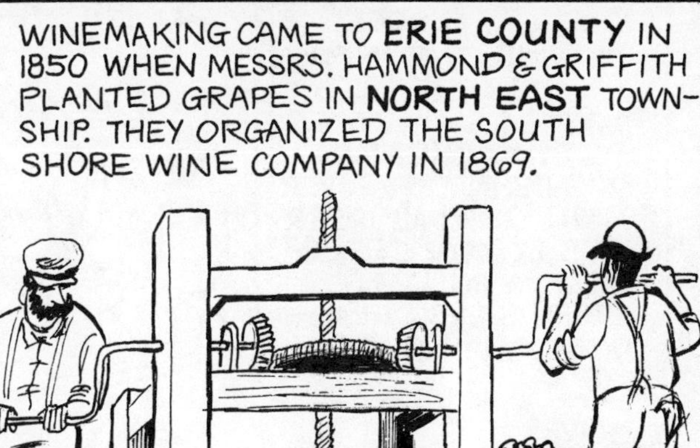

PROHIBITION (1920-33) WIPED OUT THE WINEMAKING INDUSTRY IN PENNSYLVANIA, BUT THE VINEYARDS OF **NORTH EAST** SURVIVED BY GROWING GRAPES FOR THE **WELCH GRAPE JUICE COMPANY** AT 143 S. PEARL ST.

THE LIMITED WINERY ACT OF 1968 PERMITTED THE MANUFACTURE AND SALE OF WINE BY PENNSYLVANIA RESIDENTS. SINCE THEN, PENNSYLVANIA WINES HAVE WON MEDALS & AWARDS ALL OVER THE COUNTRY.

Pennsylvania Dutch Food Lore

HOSTELS IN THE EARLY 1800's OFFERED SALADS AS MEALS IN THEMSELVES. THEY WERE OFTEN SERVED WITH CHEESE AND WARM BEER OR WINE. THE MOST POPULAR CHEESES WERE SCHTINKKEES ("STINK" CHEESE), THE PENN-DUTCH VERSION OF LIMBURGER AND SCHAPZEEGERKEES, A PUNGENT GREEN CHEESE FLAVORED WITH CLOVER.
Patrick M. Reynolds
THE PENNSYLVANIA DUTCH CALLED ASPARAGUS MICKEGRAUT, OR "FLY PLANT." IN THE DAYS BEFORE SCREENS, FOLKS HUNG MATURE ASPARAGUS PLANTS IN THEIR HOUSES TO KEEP OUT FLIES.
PARSLEY WAS PLANTED OUTSIDE BECAUSE GROWING PARSLEY INDOORS WAS CONSIDERED A PRECURSOR OF DEATH OR FUNERALS. POTTED PARSLEY WAS NO GIFT FOR A PENNSYLVANIA DUTCH FRIEND.
A MAJOR INDUSTRY IN BUCKS COUNTY DURING THE 18th AND EARLY 19th CENTURIES WAS RAISING PIGEONS FOR HUMAN CONSUMPTION.
PIGEON PIE WAS ONE OF THE MOST POPULAR BREAKFAST AND SUPPER FOODS, NEXT TO CORNMEAL MUSH.

It Started With Horseradish

WHEN HE WAS 8 YEARS OLD, HENRY JOHN PEDDLED VEGETABLES FROM THE FAMILY GARDEN DOOR TO DOOR IN **SHARPSBURG.**
Patrick M. Reynolds

AT 15, HENRY JOHN HAD FINISHED BUSINESS SCHOOL & WAS WORKING AS A BOOKKEEPER IN HIS FATHER'S BRICKYARD. DURING THE SUMMER HE MOONLIGHTED AS A *PRODUCE* HUCKSTER.

HENRY'S CUSTOMERS TOLD HIM THERE WAS A GOOD MARKET FOR HORSERADISH.

IN THOSE DAYS, WITHOUT FRESH FRUIT AND VEGETABLES IN THE WINTER, PEOPLE LIVED ON A MEAT-AND-POTATO DIET.
HORSERADISH COULD FLAVOR BLAND MEAT AND GIVE IT ***SNAP!***

BUT THERE WERE DRAWBACKS IN PREPARING HORSERADISH. THE GRATING COULD CUT A PERSON'S KNUCKLES, AND THE FUMES COULD STUN SOME FOLKS. THIS DID NOT STOP HENRY.

HE GREW LOTS OF HORSERADISH AND HIRED HIS SISTERS AND BROTHERS TO PREPARE AND BOTTLE IT. THEY SOON LEARNED HOW TO PROTECT THEIR KNUCKLES AND NOSES. THIS WAS THE BEGINNING OF THE PROCESSED FOOD EMPIRE OF **HENRY JOHN HEINZ.**

THE KETCHUP CHRONICLES
IN 1690, THE CHINESE DEVELOPED A TANGY SAUCE OF PICKLED FISH, SHELLFISH, AND SPICES TO PUT ON FISH AND FOWL. THEY CALLED IT KE-TSIAP.
ITS POPULARITY SPREAD TO MALAYA WHERE IT WAS KNOWN AS KECHAP.
MERCHANTS IN SINGAPORE SOLD THE PUREE TO ENGLISH SAILORS IN THE EARLY 18th CENTURY.
THE COOKS IN ENGLAND REPLACED THE ASIAN INGREDIENTS WITH MUSHROOMS AND LABELED IT KETCHUP.
THERE WERE ABOUT 8 VARIETIES OF KETCHUP INCLUDING WALNUT, OYSTER, LEMON, ANCHOVY, AND EVEN TOMATO.
KETCHUP WAS INTRODUCED TO AMERICA WHEN A PUBLISHER IN PHILADELPHIA PRINTED THE NEW ART OF COOKERY BY RICHARD BRIGGS IN 1792.
IT CONTAINED A RECIPE FOR TOMATO CATSUP.
Patrick M. Reynolds
KETCHUP REMAINED UNPOPULAR IN THE U.S. BECAUSE IT TOOK A LOT OF TIME AND WORK TO PREPARE.
KETCHUP BECAME AN INTEGRAL PART OF THE AMERICAN PALATE IN 1876 WHEN HENRY J. HEINZ FIGURED OUT A WAY TO MASS PRODUCE IT IN PITTSBURGH.
H.J HEINZ

JOSEPH MURGAS

WAS BORN FEB. 17, 1864 IN TAJOV, SLOVAKIA. AT 20 HE WAS STUDYING FOR THE PRIESTHOOD IN OSTRIHOM AND EXPERIMENTING IN ELECTRICITY AND WIRELESS TELEGRAPHY.

ORDAINED IN 1888, HE CONTINUED HIS EXPERIMENTS AND ALSO BECAME A RENOWNED ARTIST. MOST OF HIS PAINTINGS WERE SCENES OF SLOVAK HISTORY.

BECAUSE OF HIS REPUTATION IN THE ARTS, THE HUNGARIAN PARLIAMENT ASKED MURGAS TO EVALUATE A CANVAS DEPICTING THE OCCUPATION OF SLOVAKIA BY THE MAGYARS IN 907 A.D.

IT'S AWFUL!

IT WAS NOT WHAT THE POLITICIANS WANTED TO HEAR. THEY MADE HIS LIFE SO MISERABLE THAT HE LEFT THE COUNTRY.

ASSIGNED TO THE SACRED HEART CHURCH, **WILKES-BARRE** IN 1896, HE EXPANDED THE SERVICES OF THE PARISH AND ORGANIZED SEVERAL SLOVAK SOCIETIES.

FATHER MURGAS HAD A FEW HOBBIES: FISHING, COLLECTING BUTTERFLIES, AND PAINTING. IN 1898 HE BUILT A LABORATORY IN THE RECTORY WHERE HE INVENTED THE FORERUNNER OF **RADIO**.

The Priest Who Invented the Radio

REV. JOSEPH MURGAS WAS A SLOVAK PRIEST AT THE SACRED HEART CHURCH IN WILKES-BARRE WHEN, IN 1904, HE OBTAINED A PATENT FOR A "WIRELESS TELEGRAPHY APPARATUS."
U.S. PATENT No. 759,825

A GROUP OF FINANCIERS FROM PHILADELPHIA KNOWN AS THE UNIVERSAL AETHER COMPANY BOUGHT THE PATENT AND PLANNED TO MARKET MURGAS' INVENTION.

THEY SPENT $25,000 TO BUILD A 200 FT. TRANSMISSION TOWER IN SCRANTON & ANOTHER 19 MILES AWAY IN WILKES-BARRE BEHIND MURGAS' CHURCH.
NOTHING LIKE THESE HAD EVER BEEN CONSTRUCTED.

MURGAS TESTED HIS WIRELESS FOR SOME COMMUNITY LEADERS AND LT. CDR. SAM ROBINSON OF THE U.S. NAVY ON APRIL 27, 1905. IT WAS A SMASHING SUCCESS!

ROBINSON REPORTED TO THE NAVY DEPARTMENT,
MURGAS HAS THE BEST SYSTEM OF WIRELESS TRANSMISSION. IT WILL REVOLUTIONIZE WORLD COMMUNICATIONS.
THAT'S NICE. BUT WE'VE ALREADY CONTRACTED TO BUY RADIO EQUIPMENT FROM A MAN IN ITALY BY THE NAME OF MARCONI.

HOWEVER, MARCONI'S SYSTEM COULD ONLY TRANSMIT 15 WORDS PER MINUTE, WHILE MURGAS' RAN AT 50 W.P.M. STILL, THE GOVERNMENT WENT AHEAD WITH THE CONTRACT WITH MARCONI, SHOWN HERE.

THE INVENTOR/PRIEST

IN 1905, THE MAN WHOM HISTORY BOOKS CREDIT WITH INVENTING THE RADIO, GUGLIELMO MARCONI, VISITED FATHER J. MURGAS IN WILKES-BARRE AND ADMITTED,
MY EXPERIMENTS IN ITALY WERE SUCCESSFUL WITH SENDING WIRELESS MESSAGES ACROSS WATER, BUT NOT OVER LAND.
REALLY? I HAVE BEEN SENDING SIGNALS OVER LAND FOR MONTHS.

FATHER MURGAS WAS FORCED TO CUT BACK ON HIS EXPERIMENTS IN 1908 WHEN HIS TRANSMISSION STATION IN SCRANTON BURNED DOWN. THEN, TWO OF HIS FINANCIAL BACKERS DIED.

MEANWHILE, MARCONI AND DR. R.A. FESSENDEN INCORPORATED MANY OF MURGAS' CONCEPTS INTO A RADIO WHICH THEY PUT ON THE MARKET. BY 1912, MARCONI AND FESSENDEN WERE SUING EACH OTHER.
U.S. PATENT

FINALLY, ON JAN. 7, 1916, JUDGE MEYER OF THE U.S. DISTRICT COURT IN NEW YORK RULED,
NEITHER OF YOU INVENTED THE HIGH SPARK FREQUENCY FOR TONE TRANSMISSION.

FATHER MURGAS DIED IN 1929, AND WAS FORGOTTEN BY THE RADIO INDUSTRY. BUT, IN 1939, THE SLOVAK REPUBLIC ISSUED THIS STAMP.
SLOVENSKO
REV JOZEF MURGAS
1864
1929
60
HALIEROV
60

TODAY, A MONUMENT IN FRONT OF THE SACRED HEART CHURCH, WILKES-BARRE COMMEMORATES THE INVENTOR/ PRIEST.

POSTSCRIPT: AMONG FATHER MURGAS' MANY INVENTIONS WAS A CASTING REEL FOR A FISHING ROD WHICH HE PATENTED IN 1912.

IN 1872 ALBERT COOMBS **BARNES** WAS

Born In "The Dumps,"

THE POOREST SECTION OF SOUTH PHILADELPHIA. YOUNG BARNES LOVED TO READ, AND HE EARNED A COLLEGE SCHOLARSHIP.

HE WORKED HIS WAY THRU MEDICAL SCHOOL AT THE UNIVERSITY OF PENNSYLVANIA BY PLAYING SEMI-PRO BALL.

HE NEVER PRACTICED MEDICINE. DETERMINED TO GET RICH QUICKLY, HE SOLD DRUGS TO DOCTORS.

BARNES REALIZED HE COULD MAKE MORE MONEY WITH HIS OWN BRAND OF MEDICINE, SO HE "IMPORTED" A CHEMIST FROM HEIDELBERG, GERMANY NAMED HERMANN **HILLE.**

DR. BARNES PUT HILLE TO WORK IN A DINGY LITTLE LAB IN PHILADELPHIA.

IN 1901 HILLE CAME UP WITH AN ANTISEPTIC FOR RUNNY NOSES AND SORE THROATS WHICH THEY CALLED **ARGYROL.**

BARNES AND HILLE MADE A FORTUNE. BUT, ALTHOUGH HILLE KNEW HOW TO MAKE ARGYROL...

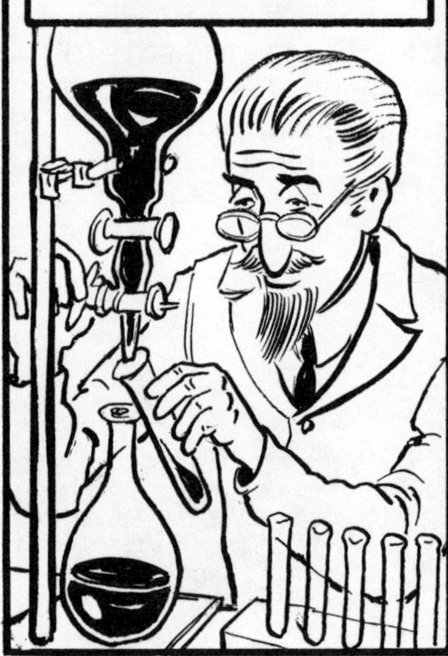

HE REFUSED TO SHARE ITS FORMULA WITH BARNES.

I DEMAND YOU GIVE ME THAT FORMULA!

BARNES' HOT TEMPER CONVINCED HILLE TO SECRETLY TAKE LESSONS IN JIUJITSU.

THE FORMULA

ARGYROL WAS A POPULAR COLD MEDICINE IN THE EARLY 1900'S, BUT ITS INVENTOR, HERMANN **HILLE** WOULD NOT REVEAL **THE** FORMULA TO HIS PARTNER, DR. ALBERT BARNES. AROUND 1907 HILLE WENT TO GERMANY TO VISIT HIS FAMILY.

MEANWHILE, DR. BARNES RIFLED THROUGH HILLE'S LABORATORY AND FOUND THE FORMULA.

AFTER HILLE RETURNED TO PHILADELPHIA, TENSION RAN HIGH BETWEEN HIM AND BARNES.

I DO ALL THE SELLING; I BRING IN THE MONEY; YOU CONTRIBUTE NOTHING.

ONE DAY HILLE THOUGHT DR. BARNES (A FORMER BOXER) WAS GOING TO SLUG HIM.

Patrick M. Reynolds

HILLE APPLIED HIS JIUJITSU!

BARNES BOUGHT OUT HILLE'S SHARE OF THE BUSINESS IN 1908 AND ESTABLISHED THE A. C. BARNES CO. IN PHILADELPHIA.

DR. BARNES HAD A UNIQUE STYLE OF MANAGEMENT. EVERY DAY HE HAD HIS 16 EMPLOYEES STOP WORKING FOR 2 HOURS TO STUDY PHILOSOPHERS SUCH AS JOHN DEWEY AND WILLIAM JAMES. DEWEY WAS A PERSONAL FRIEND OF DR. BARNES.

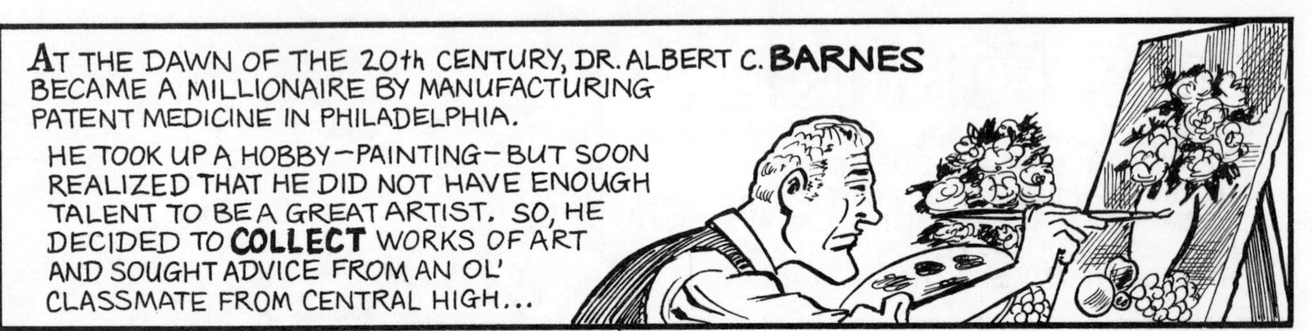
AT THE DAWN OF THE 20th CENTURY, DR. ALBERT C. BARNES BECAME A MILLIONAIRE BY MANUFACTURING PATENT MEDICINE IN PHILADELPHIA.
HE TOOK UP A HOBBY—PAINTING—BUT SOON REALIZED THAT HE DID NOT HAVE ENOUGH TALENT TO BE A GREAT ARTIST. SO, HE DECIDED TO COLLECT WORKS OF ART AND SOUGHT ADVICE FROM AN OL' CLASSMATE FROM CENTRAL HIGH...

WILLIAM GLACKENS.
AT THE TIME, 1910, GLACKENS WAS ONE OF THE TOP ILLUS-TRATORS & AVANT-GARDE ARTISTS IN AMERICA.
HE SUGGESTED,
BUY MODERN ART!
AROUND 1912 BARNES SENT GLACKENS TO PARIS WITH $20,000 TO BUY PAINTINGS FOR BARNES.
GLACKENS RETURNED WITH WORKS BY RENOIR, VAN GOGH, CEZANNE, DEGAS, MONET, GAUGUIN, & SEURAT.

A SHORT TIME LATER, BARNES HIMSELF WENT TO PARIS AND NOSED THROUGH JUNK SHOPS, CAFES, AND STUDIOS. HE DEVEL-OPED AN UNERRING EYE FOR A BARGAIN, PAYING $50 FOR HIS FIRST MATISSE.
Patrick M. Reynolds

A CANVAS BY HENRI ROUSSEAU COST HIM $10.00...

AND HE BOUGHT A PAINTING FOR $20 FROM A YOUNG ARTIST NAMED PABLO PICASSO.

THUS BEGAN THE FINEST PRIVATE COLLECTION OF MODERN ART IN THE WORLD!

Barnes' Collection

BY 1924, DR. ALBERT BARNES HAD AMASSED A COLLECTION OF MODERN ART THAT INCLUDED SOME 200 RENOIRS, 100 CEZANNES, 75 MATISSES, AND OTHER ANCIENT AND CONTEMPORARY MASTERPIECES VALUED (AT THE TIME) AT **$50 MILLION.**

HE SPENT $500,000 IN 1925 TO BUILD A MUSEUM FOR HIS COLLECTION NEXT TO HIS MANSION IN **MERION.**

AT FIRST HE OPENED HIS MUSEUM TO THE PUBLIC, BUT COULD NOT TOLERATE PEOPLE WHO BREEZED THROUGH WITHOUT STOPPING TO STUDY EVERY SINGLE PAINTING...

AND HE REALLY GOT RILED BY WHAT HE CONSIDERED *STUPID COMMENTS:*

IT'S VERY... INTERESTING.

THAT'S IT. I'M CLOSING THE MUSEUM!

BARNES HATED THE POMPOUS RICH AND TOOK PLEASURE IN RUDELY REFUSING TO LET BIG SHOTS LIKE WALTER P. CHRYSLER SEE HIS COLLECTION.

TELL THE BUM TO KEEP OUT!

AT THE SAME TIME, REMEMBERING HIS IMPOVERISHED ROOTS, HE SET UP THE BARNES FOUNDATION ON HIS ESTATE TO PROVIDE FREE ART TRAINING FOR A LIMITED NUMBER OF CAREFULLY SELECTED STUDENTS.

IN 1940 THE COLLEGE OF THE CITY OF NEW YORK FIRED THE FAMOUS BRITISH PHILOSOPHER AND MATHEMATICIAN
BERTRAND RUSSELL
BECAUSE OF HIS VIEWS ON SEX AND MORALITY. DR. ALBERT C. BARNES QUICKLY HIRED RUSSELL AT AN ANNUAL SALARY OF $8,000 TO LECTURE AT HIS *BARNES FOUNDATION* IN MERION.

BY 1943 BARNES AND RUSSELL WERE FED UP WITH EACH OTHER. BARNES FIRED THE PHILOSOPHER. RUSSELL SUED FOR BACK WAGES AND WAS AWARDED $20,000.00.

THROUGHOUT THE 1930'S AND 40'S, BARNES NEVER ALLOWED ANYONE TO SEE HIS FABULOUS ART COLLECTION EXCEPT A FEW FRIENDS SUCH AS ALBERT EINSTEIN AND JOHN DEWEY.

ON JULY 24, 1951 BARNES RAN A STOP SIGN ON RT. 29 NEAR PHOENIXVILLE, AND WAS KILLED WHEN HIS CAR WAS RAMMED BY A 10-TON TRACTOR-TRAILER. HE WAS 78 YEARS OLD.

BARNES' MUSEUM IN MERION REMAINED CLOSED FOR 9 YEARS AFTER HIS DEATH. FINALLY, THE STATE SUPREME COURT ORDERED IT, AS A TAX-EXEMPT FOUNDATION, TO OPEN ITS DOORS.

NOW, EVEN WHEN IT'S OPEN, ONLY A LIMITED NUMBER OF PEOPLE ARE ALLOWED TO ENTER.

VISITORS HOURS
Fri-Sat 9:30 AM to 4:3
Sunday 1:00 PM to 4:3
CLASSES IN SESSION MON THRU THURS
CLOSED JULY AND AUG
AND LEGAL HOLIDAYS

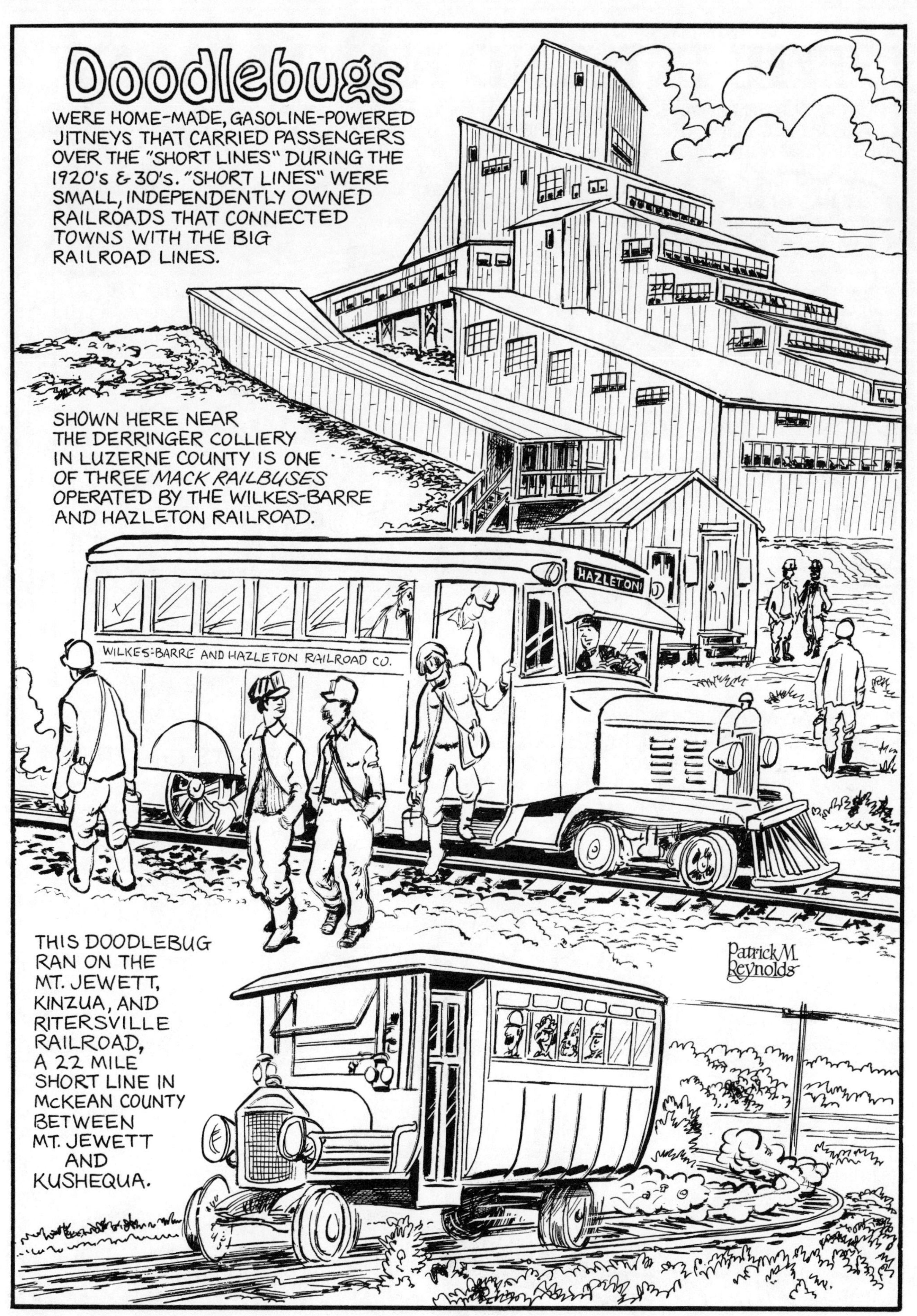
Doodlebugs
WERE HOME-MADE, GASOLINE-POWERED JITNEYS THAT CARRIED PASSENGERS OVER THE "SHORT LINES" DURING THE 1920's & 30's. "SHORT LINES" WERE SMALL, INDEPENDENTLY OWNED RAILROADS THAT CONNECTED TOWNS WITH THE BIG RAILROAD LINES.
SHOWN HERE NEAR THE DERRINGER COLLIERY IN LUZERNE COUNTY IS ONE OF THREE MACK RAILBUSES OPERATED BY THE WILKES-BARRE AND HAZLETON RAILROAD.
HAZLETON
WILKES-BARRE AND HAZLETON RAILROAD CO.
THIS DOODLEBUG RAN ON THE MT. JEWETT, KINZUA, AND RITERSVILLE RAILROAD, A 22 MILE SHORT LINE IN McKEAN COUNTY BETWEEN MT. JEWETT AND KUSHEQUA.
Patrick M. Reynolds

THE INLAND NAVAL BASE

JUST AFTER THE JAPANESE BOMBED PEARL HARBOR (DEC.7,1941), THE TOP BRASS IN THE U.S.NAVY SAW THE NEED FOR A SUPPLY DEPOT..

THE GOVERNMENT PAID $100 AN ACRE FOR 841 ACRES OF FARM LAND JUST OUTSIDE MECHANICSBURG. CONSTRUCTION BEGAN ON NEW YEAR'S DAY, 1942. BY JULY, 8,400 EMPLOYEES WERE BUILDING THE DEPOT.

IT HAS TO BE FAR ENOUGH INLAND TO BE SAFE FROM AN ATTACK...
YET CLOSE TO ROADS, RAILLINES AND AIRPORTS...
...TO EASILY REACH THE MAJOR EAST COAST PORTS.

THE ADMIRALS COMMISSIONED THE **NAVAL SUPPLY DEPOT, MECHANICSBURG** ON OCT.1, 1942. FOR THE NEXT 3 YEARS, SOME 9,800 EMPLOYEES, BOTH CIVILIAN AND MILITARY, SUPPLIED AMERICA'S WAR FLEET WITH REPAIR PARTS. SHOWN HERE IS A SHIP'S DIESEL ENGINE.

SINCE 1945, THE MAIN ACTIVITY AT THE DEPOT HAS BEEN THE **SHIPS PARTS CONTROL CENTER** WHICH EMPLOYS OVER 4,000 PEOPLE. THE CENTER PURCHASES ABOUT $1½ BILLION WORTH OF WEAPON SYSTEMS PARTS PER YEAR AND CONTROLS A WORLD-WIDE INVENTORY OF MORE THAN 500,000 ITEMS WORTH **$15½ BILLION.**

Patrick M. Reynolds

WELL, WHADDYA KNOW!
THE PONY EXPRESS
WAS NOT LIMITED TO THE WILD WEST.
IN 1835 IT RAN ON THE NATIONAL PIKE (U.S. Rt. 40) BETWEEN WASHINGTON, D.C. AND CINCINNATI, OHIO.
ONE OF THE PENNSYLVANIA RIDERS WAS
THOMAS WILEY
WHO CARRIED THE MAIL FROM UNIONTOWN, HIS HOME TOWN, TO WASHINGTON, PA.
US
CHROME,
WHICH IS USED IN THE MANUFACTURE OF STAINLESS STEEL, COMES FROM THE MINERAL CHROMITE.
FROM 1827 TO 1882 THE WOOD MINE IN SOUTHCENTRAL PENNSYLVANIA WAS THE LARGEST PRODUCER OF CHROMITE IN THE WORLD.
THE FIRST STATE GAME LAND WAS AN AREA OF OVER 6,200 ACRES NEAR GLEN HAZEL, ELK COUNTY.
THE PENNSYLVANIA GAME COMMISSION PURCHASED THE TRACT IN 1920.
THE ONLY TOMB OF AN
UNKNOWN SOLDIER
OF THE REVOLUTIONARY WAR IS ON FIRST AVENUE IN BETHLEHEM, PENNSYLVANIA. HE DIED IN THE SINGLE BRETHREN'S HOUSE WHICH WAS USED AS A MILITARY HOSPITAL IN 1776 AND 1777.
Patrick M. Reynolds

Here is a sample of Mr. Reynolds' Texas cartoon which appears weekly in several Texas newspapers, and is also available as a series of books.

TEXAS LORE by Patrick M Reynolds

THE BRUNT OF THE HURRICANE

HIT GALVESTON AT 6 PM, SEPT. 8, 1900. WINDS OF 120 MPH TORE THE 2½ TON BELL FROM ST. MARY'S CATHEDRAL AS IT WAS TOLLING THE ANGELUS.

IN THE RECTORY NEARBY, BISHOP NICHOLAS GALLAGHER TURNED TO FATHER JAMES KIRWIN, GESTURED TO THE OTHER CLERGYMEN, AND SAID, "PREPARE THESE PRIESTS FOR DEATH."

NEXT, A TIDAL WAVE ROARED OVER THE ISLAND, SMASHING HOUSES TO SPLINTERS & HURLING WRECKAGE AGAINST STRUCTURES FARTHER INLAND.

WITHIN MINUTES THE CALAMITY KILLED ALMOST 8,000 PEOPLE AND DESTROYED $17 MILLION WORTH OF PROPERTY. IT WAS THE WORST RECORDED NATURAL DISASTER THAT HAD BEFALLEN NORTH AMERICA.

Mr. Reynolds' cartoon on the history of New York City appears every Sunday in the color comics section of New York Newsday and is available as a book.

Big Apple Almanac by Patrick M. Reynolds

TAXI!

IN 1891, WILHELM BRUHN OF GERMANY INVENTED A DEVICE TO COMPUTE TIME AND DISTANCE TRAVELED BY A VEHICLE. THE FRENCH CALLED IT A *TAXI-MÈTRE*, MEANING METER FOR MEASURING A TAX OR FARE. IT WORKED SO WELL THAT THE CABBIES IN FRANKFURT THREW BRUHN INTO THE RIVER.

ONE DAY IN 1907, HARRY N. ALLEN TOOK A CAB FROM 44th ST. TO 58th ST. IN MANHATTAN. WHEN THE DRIVER CHARGED HIM $5 FOR THE 3/4 MILE RIDE, ALLEN GOT SO IRRITATED THAT HE DECIDED TO REVOLUTIONIZE THE CAB BUSINESS.
11/13
PR

MANY PEOPLE DON'T RIDE CABS BECAUSE THEY'RE OVERPRICED.
ALLEN BORROWED $3 MILLION, MOSTLY FROM EUROPEAN BACKERS, AND PUT 65 NEW CABS WITH UNIFORMED DRIVERS ON THE STREETS OF NEW YORK.

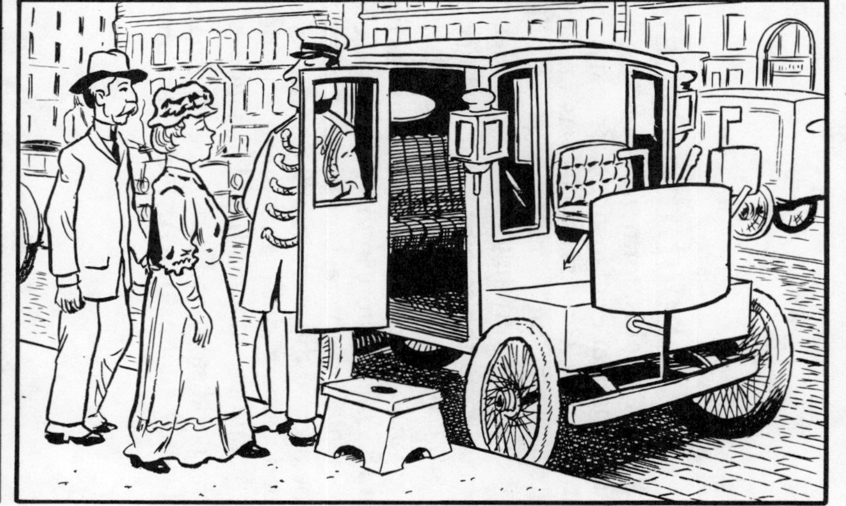
MR. ALLEN CALLED HIS NEW FIRM THE NEW YORK TAXICAB ASSOCIATION BECAUSE HE EQUIPPED HIS VEHICLES WITH *TAXI-MÈTRES*. THUS, A NEW WORD ORIGINATED IN THE BIG APPLE— **TAXICAB.**

Big Apple Almanac and Texas Lore are available in book form.
For a catalog, send $1.00 to
The Red Rose Studio, 358 Flintlock Drive, The Town of Willow Street, PA 17584

About the Artist-Author

Patrick M. Reynolds, formerly of Minersville, PA., earned a Bachelor of Fine Arts degree at Pratt Institute, Brooklyn, N.Y. and a Masters in Illustration at Syracuse University. He was an advertising agency art director before serving as an Army Intelligence officer in the Vietnam Conflict (1967-68) and is currently in the Army Reserve.

He is married to the former Patricia Gouldner of Schuylkill Haven, PA. They have three children: Kimberly Jo, Maria Alyssa, and Thomas Patrick.

A visit to the Johnstown Flood Museum was Reynolds' first step in researching the 1889 flood story in this book. He viewed the museum's 15 minute slide presentation several times to take notes and compile a rough outline. Then he divided the story into five parts: before the flood to set the scene, the flood coming down the valley, the destruction of Johnstown, the recovery, and the aftermath and litigation.

After the flood story had run in the newspapers, the original artwork was exhibited in the Johnstown Art Museum during the Centennial Observance.

TEXAS LORE
Pennsylvania Profiles
Profiles
TEXAS LORE
SABINE COUNTY